BENJAMIN BRITTEN

Les Illuminations
de Rimbaud

Vocal Score

BOOSEY AND HAWKES

Benjamin Britten, *1913-1976.*

Les [Illuminations, arr.]

for Soprano or Tenor Voice
and String Orchestra

Poems by Arthur Rimbaud

Op. 18

Vocal Score by the Composer

Boosey & Hawkes
Music Publishers Limited
London · Paris · Bonn · Johannesburg · Sydney · Toronto · New York

am

At various times during the period which covers Rimbaud's visit to Verlaine in Paris (1871), the escapade of the two poets in Belgium and London, and the 19-year old boy's return to his home at Charleville (1873), was written the curious, haphazard collection of hermetic pieces which Verlaine, after Rimbaud's death, published under the title of "Les Illuminations." The title was Verlaine's, though one may suppose it to have been at least suggested to him by chance remarks the author must have made regarding the poems during their life together. The titles of some of the pieces were bestowed by successive editors, while others (e.g. "Being Beauteous") are clearly the poet's own. The separation of the work into verse and prose is also arbitrary, since Rimbaud composed simultaneously in both media. The poems do, however, fall into three main divisions, according to the times at which they were written: the visionary and prophetic pieces belonging to the Paris period; the descriptions of Flemish and Belgian towns to the poet's desultory journey; and finally pieces like "*Solde*" and "*Départ*," which were written last and look forward to "*Une Saison en Enfer*" and beyond it, to Rimbaud's renunciation of literature in favour of the life of action.

Those who insist upon knowing what a poem *means* (in the narrower sense) cannot in this case be satisfied. All these short pieces must be considered in the light of (1) the title, which makes play with two meanings: the medieval illuminated manuscript and the sense of casting light upon a specified scene; (2) Rimbaud's expressed intention of searching for a new use of language in which words and phrases should be used like notes and harmonies in music. The first meaning is justified by the sharpness and exactitude of the images; the second by the way in which they are juxtaposed. Rimbaud in fact suppresses the simile: the word "like" has no place in the vocabulary of his later work; the thing and that with which it is compared, become a single image, the meaning of which has to be felt, rather than apprehended, like a phrase of music. Yet it is always a picture, not an idea, that is evoked, and Britten's settings have rightly the sharp outlines and vivid colours of a missal. This point is important, for these poems are only obscure in the sense that, as Rimbaud says, the ultimate key to them is in his keeping alone. Taken separately, they explain, or rather express themselves, like elliptical entries in a diary.

The composer's choice was evidently governed, at least to some extent, by what would set effectively. Yet, as the final episodes indicate, the guiding thread is the transition from one phase of life to another — as it were from the reckless experiments of adolescence (*Villes, Phrases, Being Beauteous*) to the disillusioned, but clarified intentions of maturity: "Departure amid fresh love and fresh sounds." So that this is the opposite of nostalgic music: it looks forward, with the microscopic vision and the ruthless energy of discovered power.

Edward Sackville West.

Pauses between movements should be as short as possible.

The French words are reprinted by permission of Mercure de France, Paris, the English translations by Helen Rootham are reprinted from " Prose Poems from Les Illuminations of Arthur Rimbaud " by permission of Messrs. Faber & Faber, Ltd., London.

Frontispiece :   Portrait sketch of Arthur Rimbaud by Paul Verlaine.

I. FANFARE. J'ai seul la clef de cette parade sauvage.

II. VILLES. Ce sont des villes ! C'est un peuple pour qui se sont montés ces 'Alleghanys et cés Libans de rêve ! Des chalets de cristal et de bois se meuvent sur des rails et des poulies invisibles. Les vieux cratères ceints de colosses et de palmiers de cuivre rugissent mélodieusement dans les feux . . . Des cortèges de Mabs en robes rousses, opalines, montent des ravines. Là-haut, les pieds dans la cascade et les ronces, les cerfs tettent Diane. Les Bacchantes des banlieues sanglotent et la lune brûle et hurle. Vénus entre dans les cavernes des forgerons et des ermites. Des groupes de beffrois chantent les idées des peuples. Des châteaux bâtis en os sort la musique inconnue . . . . Le paradis des orages s'effondre. Les sauvages dansent sans cesse la Fête de la Nuit.
. . . . .
Quels bons bras, quelle belle heure me rendront cette région d'où viennent mes sommeils et mes moindres mouvements ?

IIIa. PHRASE. J'ai tendu des cordes de clocher à clocher; des guirlandes de fenêtre à fenêtre; des chaînes d'or d'étoile à étoile, et je danse.

IIIb. ANTIQUE. Gracieux fils de Pan! Autour de ton front couronné de fleurettes et de baies, tes yeux, des boules précieuses, remuent. Tachées de lie brune, tes joues se creusent. Tes crocs luisent. Ta poitrine ressemble à une cithare, des tintements circulent dans tes bras blonds. Ton coeur bat dans ce ventre où dort le double sexe. Promène-toi, la nuit, en mouvant doucement cette cuisse, cette seconde cuisse et cette jambe de gauche.

IV. ROYAUTÉ. Un beau matin, chez un peuple fort doux, un homme et une femme superbes criaient sur la place publique : "Mes amis, je veux qu'elle soit reine!" "Je veux être reine!" Elle riait et tremblait. Il parlait aux amis de révélation, d'épreuve terminée. Ils se pâmaient l'un contre l'autre.
En effet, ils furent rois toute une matinée, où les tentures carminées se relevèrent sur les maisons, et tout l'après-midi, où ils s'avancèrent du côté des jardins de palmes.

V. MARINE. Les chars d'argent et de cuivre,
Les proues d'acier et d'argent,
Battent l'écume,
Soulèvent les souches des ronces.
Les courants de la lande,
Et les ornières immenses du reflux,
Filent circulairement vers l'est,
Vers les piliers de la forêt,
Vers les fûts de la jetée,
Dont l'angle est heurté par des tourbillons de lumière.

I. FANFARE. I alone hold the key to this savage parade.

II. TOWNS. These are towns ! It is for the inhabitants of towns that these dream Alleghanies and Lebanons have been raised. Castles of crystal and wood move on rails and invisible pulleys. Old craters, encircled with colossal statues and palms of copper, roar melodiously in their fires. . . . . Corteges of Queen Mabs in robes red and opaline, climb the ravines. Up there, their hoofs in the cascades and the briars, the stags give Diana suck. Bacchantes of the suburbs weep, and the moon burns and howls. Venus enters the caves of the blacksmiths and hermits. Groups of bell-towers sing aloud the ideas of the people. From castles built of bones proceeds unknown music. . . . . The paradise of the thunders bursts and falls. Savages dance unceasingly the Festival of the Night.
. . . . .
What kindly arms, what good hour will restore to me those regions from which come my slumbers and the least of my movements ?

IIIa. PHRASE. I have hung ropes from bell-tower to bell-tower; garlands from window to window; golden chains from star to star—and I dance.

IIIb. ANTIQUE. Oh, gracious son of Pan! Thine eyes —those precious globes—glance slowly; thy brow is crowned with little flowers and berries. Thy hollow cheeks are spotted with brown lees; thy tusks shine. Thy breast resembles a cithara; tinkling sounds run through thy blond arms. Thy heart beats in that womb where sleeps Hermaphrodite. Walk at night, softly moving this thigh, this other thigh, this left leg.

IV. ROYALTY. On a beautiful morning, in a country inhabited by a mild and gentle people, a man and woman of proud presence stood in the public square and cried aloud : "My friends, it is my wish that she should be queen." She laughed and trembled. To his friends he spoke of a revelation, of a test concluded. Swooningly they leaned one against the other.
And during one whole morning, whilst the crimson hangings were displayed on the houses, and during the whole afternoon, while they advanced towards the palm gardens, they were indeed kings.

V. MARINE. Chariots of silver and of copper
Prows of steel and of silver
Beat the foam,
Life the stems of the brambles.
The streams of the barren parts
And the immense tracks of the ebb
Flow circularly towards the east,
Towards the pillars of the forest,
Towards the piles of the jetty,
Against whose angles are hurled whirlpools of light.

VI. INTERLUDE. J'ai seul la clef de cette parade sauvage.

VII. BEING BEAUTEOUS. Devant une neige, un Etre de beauté de haute taille. Des sifflements de mort et des cercles de musique sourde font monter, s'élargir et trembler comme un spectre ce corps adoré ; des blessures écarlates et noires éclatent dans les chairs superbes.—Les couleurs propres de la vie se foncent, dansent et se dégagent autour de la vision, sur le chantier.—Et les frissons s'élèvent et grondent, et la saveur forcenée de ces effets se chargeant avec les sifflements mortels et les rauques musiques que le monde, loin derrière nous, lance sur notre mère de beauté,—elle recule, elle se dresse. Oh ! nos os sont revêtus d'un nouveau corps amoureux.

O la face centrée, l'écusson de crin, les bras de cristal ! le canon sur lequel je dois m'abattre à travers la mêlée des arbres et de l'air léger !

VIII. PARADE. Des drôles très solides. Plusieurs ont exploité vos mondes. Sans besoins, et peu pressés de mettre en oeuvre leurs brillantes facultés et leur expérience de vos consciences. Quels hommes mûrs ! Des yeux hébétés à la façon de la nuit d'été, rouges et noirs, tricolorés, d'acier piqué d'étoiles d'or ; des facies déformés, plombés, blêmis, incendiés ; des enrouements folâtres ! La démarche cruelle des oripeaux !—Il y a quelques jeunes—

. . . . .

O le plus violent Paradis de la grimace enragée ! . . . . Chinois, Hottentots, Bohémiens, niais, hyènes, Molochs, vieilles démences, démons sinistres, ils mêlent les tours populaires, maternels, avec les poses et les tendresses bestiales. Ils interpréteraient des pièces nouvelles et des chansons " bonnes filles ". Maîtres jongleurs, ils transforment le lieu et les personnes et usent de la comédie magnétique.

. . . . .

J'ai seul la clef de cette parade sauvage.

IX. DÉPART. Assez vu. La vision s'est rencontrée à tous les airs.
Assez eu. Rumeurs des villes, le soir, et au soleil, et toujours.
Assez connu. Les arrêts de la vie.—O Rumeurs et Visions !
Départ dans l'affection et le bruit neufs.

VI. INTERLUDE. I alone hold the key to this savage parade.

VII. BEING BEAUTEOUS. Against a background of snow is a beautiful Being of majestic stature. Death is all round her, and whistling, dying breaths, and circles of hollow music, cause this adored body to rise, to swell, and to tremble like a spectre. Scarlet and black wounds break out on the superb flesh. Colours which belong to life deepen, dance, and separate themselves around the vision, upon the path. Shudders rise and mutter ; and the mad savour of all these things, heavy with dying groans and raucous music, is hurled at our Mother of Beauty by the world far behind us. She recoils, she stands erect. Oh rapture ! Our bones are covered anew with a body of love.

Ah ! The pale ashen face, the mane-like hair, the arms of crystal. And there is the cannon upon which I must cast myself through the noise of trees and light winds.

VIII. PARADE. These are very sturdy rogues. Many of them have made use of you and your like. Without wants, they are in no hurry to put into action their brilliant faculties and their experience of your consciences. What mature men ! Here are sottish eyes out of a midsummer night's dream—red, black, tricoloured ; eyes of steel spotted with golden stars ; deformed faces, leaden-hued, livid, enflamed ; wanton hoarseness. They have the ungainly bearing of rag dolls. There are youths among them—

. . . .

It is a violent Paradise of mad grimaces. . . . . Chinese, Hottentots, gypsies, simpletons, hyænas, Molochs, old insanities, sinister demons, they alternate popular or maternal tricks with bestial poses and caresses. They can interpret modern plays or songs of a simple naivety at will. Master jugglers, they transform places and people, and make use of magnetic comedy.

. . . . .

I alone hold the key to this savage parade.

IX. DEPARTURE. Sufficiently seen.—The vision has been met in all guises.
Sufficiently heard.— Rumours of the town at night, in the sunlight, at all times.
Sufficiently known.—Life's decrees.
Oh Rumours ! Oh Vision !
Departure in the midst of love and new rumours.

For Sophie Wyss

LES ILLUMINATIONS

Poems by
A. RIMBAUD

Music by
BENJAMIN BRITTEN, Op. 18

I. FANFARE

WINTHROP ROGERS EDITION
Copyright **1944** in U.S.A. by Hawkes & Son (London) Ltd.
Copyright for all countries

Printed in England

Fanfare

II. VILLES

11

Villes

H. 15592

Ce sont des vil - les! Des cor-tè - ges de Mabs en ro - bes rous-ses, o-pa-li - nes, mon-tent des ra - vi - nes. Là-haut, les pieds dans la cas-cade et les ron - ces, les cerfs tet-tent Di - a - ne. Les Bac-

-chan - tes des ban - lieu - es san - glo - tent et la lu - ne

brûle et hur - le. Vé - nus en - tre dans les ca-

-ver - nes des for - ge - rons et............ des......... er -

-mi - tes. Ce sont des.....

Des grou - pes de bef - frois chan - tent les i - dé - es des peu - ples.

Des châ - teaux bâ - tis en os sort....... la mu - sique in - con - nu - e.

Ce sont des vil - les!

Ce sont des vil - les!

Villes

H. 15592

Le pa-ra-dis des o-ra-ges s'ef-fon - - - - dre.

Les sau-va - ges dan-sent sans ces - se, dan - sent, dan-sent sans ces-se la

Fê-te de la Nuit. Ce sont des vil - - - - les!

Quels bons bras,

quel - le belle heu - re me ren-dront cet - te ré - gion d'où

vien-nent mes som - meils et mes moin - dres mou - ve -

- ments?

IIIª PHRASE

To K.H.W.S.

IIIb ANTIQUE

H. 15592

IV. ROYAUTÉ

Un beau ma - tin, chez un peu-ple fort doux, un homme et u - ne

fem-me su-per-bes cri-aient, cri-aient sur la pla - ce pub-lique:

2 *risoluto*

"Mes a-mis, mes a-mis, je veux qu'elle soit

p marcato

molto staccato

rei - ne, je veux qu'elle soit rei-ne!" "Je veux ê-tre rei-ne, ê-tre

cresc.

rei - ne, ê-tre rei-ne!" Elle riait............. et trem-blait.

Il par-lait aux a-mis de ré-vé-la-ti - on, d'é-
preu - ve ter-mi - né - e. Ils se pâ-mai - ent l'un con-tre
l'au - tre.
En ef-fet, ils fu-rent rois

8ve ad lib.

sempre stacc.

V. MARINE

-rants de la lande, Et les or - nières im - men - ses du re -

flux, Fi-lent cir-cu-lair' - - ment vers

l'est, Vers les pi - liers

de la fo rêt,............ Vers les fûts

V. MARINE

de la je - té - e,
Dont
l'angle est heur - té par des
tour-bil - lons,......
tour-bil - lons......................
de.... lu -
-mie - - - - - - - - re.

con forza

cresc.

rall.

a tempo

ten.

To E.M.

VI. INTERLUDE

J'ai seul la clef de cet-te pa-ra - de, de

cet-te pa-ra - de sau - va - - - ge.

Attacca subito

To P.N.L.P.

VII. BEING BEAUTEOUS

Being Beauteous

Being Beauteous

Being Beauteous

34

bras de cris - tal!............. le ca - non sur le - quel je dois

m'abattre à tra - - vers la mê - lé - e des arbres.............. et de

l'air lé - - ger!

Being Beauteous

H. 15592

VIII. PARADE

Parade

Parade

IX. DÉPART

[Amityville, N.Y. — Oct. 25th 1939]